Rhapsody In Blue
& 45 Creative Piano Solos

compiled and edited by Dan Coates

RHAPSODY IN BLUE

By
GEORGE GERSHWIN

Moderately slow, with expression

CHARIOTS OF FIRE

Music by
VANGELIS
Arranged by
Dan Coates

EVERGREEN
(Love Theme From "A STAR IS BORN")
FIRST ARTISTS Presents A BARWOOD-JON PETERS Production of "A STAR IS BORN"

Words by
PAUL WILLIAMS

Music by
BARBRA STREISAND
Arranged by DAN COATES

Moderately slow, flowing

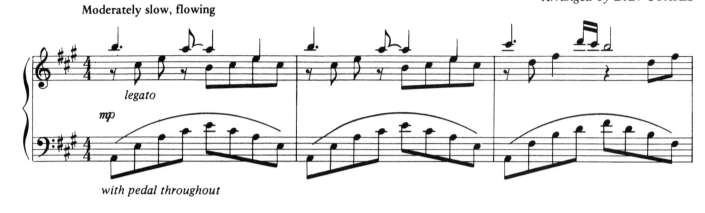

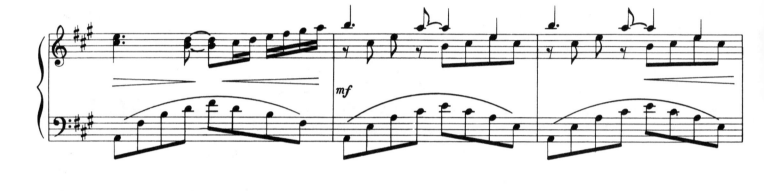

FASCINATING RHYTHM

Music and Lyrics by
GEORGE GERSHWIN and IRA GERSHWIN

ARTHUR'S THEME
(Best That You Can Do)

From "ARTHUR" an ORION PICTURES release through WARNER BROS.

Words and Music by
**BURT BACHARACH, CAROLE BAYER SAGER,
CHRISTOPHER CROSS and PETER ALLEN**

Moderately

THE OLD SONGS

Words and Music by
DAVID POMERANZ and BUDDY KAYE

Moderate Ballad

NOSTALGIA

Piano Solo

By
DAVID ROSE

POOR BUTTERFLY

By
RAYMOND HUBBELL

Slowly, with much expression

FLY ME TO THE MOON
(In Other Words)

Words and Music b
BART HOWARD

THE MASTERPIECE
(Theme From "THE MASTERPIECE THEATRE")

By
J.J. MOURET
PAUL PARNES

Majestically

Moderate Rock Beat

To Coda II

To Coda I

mf

CONCERTO IN F
(Second Movement)

By
GEORGE GERSHWIN

TEMPTATION RAG

Words by
LOUIS WESLYN

Music by
HENRY LODGE

Allegretto con moto. M.M. ♩ = 108.

TEA FOR TWO

Words by
IRVING CAESAR

Music by
VINCENT YOUMAN

THEME FROM THE SUNDOWNERS

By
DIMITRI TIOMKI

Moderately slow

Broadly

STOUTHEARTED MEN

Words by
OSCAR HAMMERSTEIN II

Music by
SIGMUND ROMBERG

12TH STREET RAG

Words and Music by
EUDAY L. BOWMAN

THE TOY TRUMPET

By
RAYMOND SCOTT

Words and Music by
RAYMOND SCOTT

EMBRACEABLE YOU

Music and Lyrics by
GEORGE GERSHWIN and IRA GERSHWIN

I GOT RHYTHM

Music and Lyrics by
GEORGE GERSHWIN and IRA GERSHWIN

62

AUTUMN NOCTURNE

Words by
KIM GANNON

Music by
JOSEF MYROW

Andante mosso

MEMORIES

Words by
GUS KAHN

Music by
EGBERT VAN ALSTYNE

THE DESERT SONG

Words by
OTTO HARBACH and OSCAR HAMMERSTEIN II

Music by
SIGMUND ROMBERG

Valse moderato

CANADIAN CAPERS

By
GUS CHANDLER, BERT WHITE
and HENRY COHEN

(the bass notes indicated thus: ◊ may be omitted and bass board struck with the foot.)

INDIAN LOVE CALL

Words by
OTTO HARBACH and OSCAR HAMMERSTEIN II

Music by
RUDOLF FRIML

THE MAN I LOVE

Music and Lyrics by
GEORGE GERSHWIN and IRA GERSHWIN

Slow and in a swinging style

KISS ME AGAIN

Words by
HENRY BLOSSOM

Music by
VICTOR HERBERT

THE JAPANESE SANDMAN

Words by
RAYMOND B. EGAN

Music by
RICHARD A. WHITING

RIALTO RIPPLES
(RAG)

By
GEORGE GERSHWIN
and WILL DONALDSON

Marcato

TRIO

D. S. al Fine

SHADOW WALTZ

Words by
AL DUBIN

Music by
HARRY WARREN

THE IMPERIAL MARCH
(Darth Vaders' Theme)

Music by
JOHN WILLIAMS

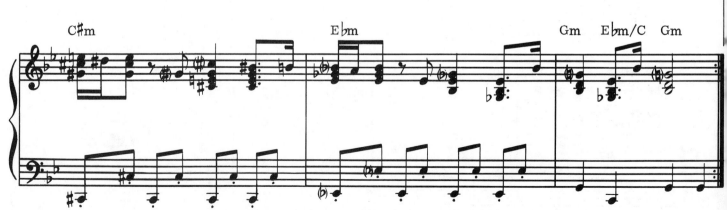

FONTAINEBLEAU

By
TADD DAMERON

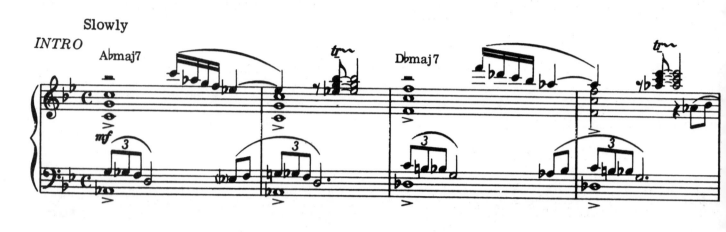

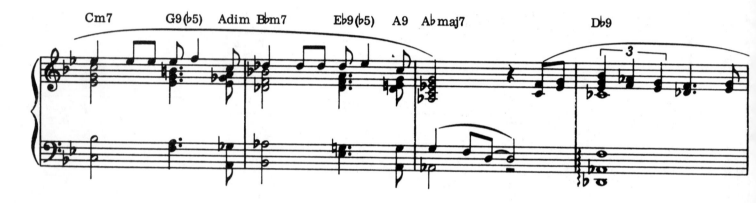

"THE SWAN"

"FAREWELL"

* Small notes optional for Right Hand, with the Left Hand playing the melody an octave lower than written.

ZIGEUNER

Words and Music by
NOEL COWARD

TILL WE MEET AGAIN

Words by
RAYMOND B. EGAN

Music by
RICHARD A. WHITING

WANTING YOU

Words by
OSCAR HAMMERSTEIN II

Music by
SIGMUND ROMBERG

SOMEBODY LOVES ME

Words by
B.G. DeSYLVA and BALLARD MACDONALD

Music by
GEORGE GERSHWIN

Allegro moderato

108

ONE ALONE

Words by
OTTO HARBACH and OSCAR HAMMERSTEIN II

Music by
SIGMUND ROMBERG

'S WONDERFUL

Music and Lyrics by
GEORGE GERSHWIN and IRA GERSHWIN

MY BUDDY

Words by
GUS KAHN

Music by
WALTER DONALDSON

LIMEHOUSE BLUES

Words by
DOUGLAS FURBER

Music by
PHILIP BRAHAM

I'LL SEE YOU AGAIN

By
NOEL COWARD

JALOUSIE
(Jealousy)

Words by
VERA BLOOM
Spanish Words by
BELEN ORTEGA

Music by
JACOB GADE

Tango D.C. ad lib.

GYPSY LOVE SONG

Words by
HARRY B. SMITH

Music by
VICTOR HERBERT

Molto tranquillo

AH! SWEET MYSTERY OF LIFE

Words by
RIDA JOHNSON YOUNG

Music by
VICTOR HERBERT

LOVER, COME BACK TO ME

Words by
OSCAR HAMMERSTEIN II

Music by
SIGMUND ROMBERG

LIZA
(All The Clouds'll Roll Away)

Words by
IRA GERSHWIN and GUS KAHN

Music by
GEORGE GERSHWIN

FOUR-TWENTY, A.M.

By
DAVID ROSE

144